EAST 17 · STEAM

Exclusive Distributors:
Music Sales Limited
8/9 Frith Street, London W1V 5TZ, England.
Music Sales Pty Limited
120 Rothschild Avenue, Rosebery, NSW 2018, Australia.

This book © Copyright 1994 by Wise Publications.
Order No. AM927916
ISBN 0-7119-4867-4

Music arranged by Roger Day.
Music processed by Paul Ewers Music Design.

Your Guarantee of Quality:
As publishers, we strive to produce every book to
the highest commercial standards. The music has been
freshly engraved and, whilst endeavouring to retain the
original running order of the recorded album, this book
has been carefully designed to minimise awkward page
turns and to make playing from it a real pleasure.

Particular care has been given to specifying acid-free,
neutral-sized paper made from pulps which have not been
elemental chlorine bleached.

This pulp is from farmed sustainable forests and
was produced with special regard for the environment.
Throughout, the printing and binding have been planned
to ensure a sturdy, attractive publication which should
give years of enjoyment. If your copy fails to meet our high
standards, please inform us and we will gladly replace it.

Music Sales' complete catalogue describes thousands
of titles and is available in full colour sections by subject,
direct from Music Sales Limited. Please state your areas
of interest and send a cheque/postal order for £1.50 for
postage to: Music Sales Limited, Newmarket Road,
Bury St. Edmunds, Suffolk IP33 3YB.

Printed in the United Kingdom by
J.B. Offset Printers (Marks Tey) Limited, Marks Tey, Essex.

8.95

Wise Publications
London/New York/Paris/Sydney/Copenhagen/Madrid

STEAM

Words & Music by Mortimer, Stannard & Rowebottom.

4

night let's be-come___ one soul. Steam, steam,___ steam,___ steam.___

The clock up-on your wall is tick-ing slow-er and slow-er,

time dis-ap-pears as I go low-er and low-er, I know your fi-nal fan-ta-sy, but I can't re-peat__ that

5

Verse 2:

Steam, like a cream dream, never stop rising
I'll rub you like a wave going out while the tide's in
Precious bubbilicious, hard or nice 'n' easy
Smooth with the move to sooth, dry or greasy
Here is your harmony, here is your friend,
Kindred spirit of ethereal blend
Meet me on a cloud, go on a journey,
Sure I'll take your body on a mystery tour.

HOLD MY BODY TIGHT

Words & Music by Mortimer, Stannard & Rowebottom.

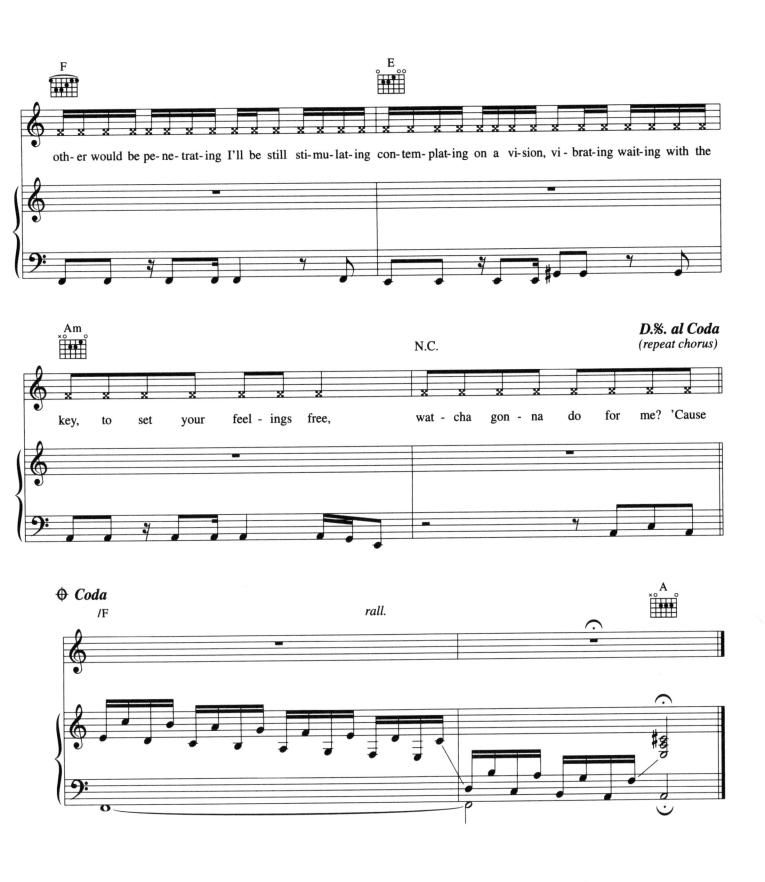

Verse 2:
My body's all alone
Need someone to take me home
Talk until the morning light
Don't wanna do ya, just hold you tight.

LET IT ALL GO

Words & Music by Mortimer, Coldwell, Kean & Hawken.

Let it all go, let it all go.

Let it all go, let it all go.

Let it all go, let it all go.

Let it all go, let it all go.

Twist - ing turn - ing with your bo - dy, ea -

sy feel free and then go a lit - tle cra - zy, ne - ver slip and slide, take it ea - sy, move and glide, take you

on a lit - tle ride on - to a dance hall vibe. Here we go with the flow, let your love go, bro - ther don't

13

smo-ther your lo-ver 'cause I'm go-ing un-der-co-ver. What's go-ing on in this world to-day, as I

lay on my bed, I pray oh by the way.

N.C.

East se-ven-teen, ah yes, here we go, sounds of the bass, now go with the flow.

Free your mind, your bo-dy and soul and let the mu-sic take con-trol.

Let it all go, let it all go, let it all go to a tem-po roll and rum-ble.

Ne-ver tum-ble 'cause you know I ne-ver stum-ble cool and hum-ble, I buzz you like a bum-ble

bee.
Let it all go, let it all go.   Let it all go, let it all go.

Let it all go, let it all go.   Let it all go, let it all go.

1.

Let it all go, let it all go.   We're gon - na rock ya, we're gon - na rock ya.

Let it all go, let it all go.   We're gon - na rock ya, we're gon - na rock ya.

SET ME FREE

Words & Music by Mortimer.

*This song is transcribed here in A minor for ease of
playing – a semitone up from the recorded version*

real - ly love the lo - ving that you're gi - ving to me— since you came in - to my life and set me
Set me

Am

free.
free,   set ev - 'ry-bo-dy free,   set me free,   set ev - 'ry-bo-dy

G/A

Am

free,   set me free,   set ev - 'ry-bo-dy free,   set me

G/A

free,   set ev - 'ry-bo-dy free.

Verse 2:
All I ever dreamed of
Walked into my life
No more boring days
No more lonely nights
So c'mon darling
Give in to me
Come inside my soul
C'mon and set me free.

Verse 3:
I was lonely
I was so afraid
And with the sunshine
Into my life you came
You made it brighter
So that I could see
You hypnotise my mind
And came and set me free.

STAY ANOTHER DAY

Words & Music by Mortimer, Kean & Hawken.

Ba-by if you've got to go — a — way,— don't think I can take the pain—

— won't you stay a-no-ther day.—

Play 1º only

Play 2º only

27

and try to throw— it all— a-way.—

Thought I heard— you say— you love— me, that your love—

was gon-na be— here to stay.—

I've on-ly just be-gun— to know— you, all I can say—

is won't you stay— just one more day.—

2.

Ba - by if you've got to go— a - way,— don't think I can take the pain—

won't you stay an - oth - er day.—

29

Verse 2:
I touch your face while you are sleeping
And hold your hand
Don't understand what's going on
Good times we had return to haunt me
Though it's for you
All that I do seems to be wrong.

AROUND THE WORLD

Words & Music by Mortimer, Harvey, Rowebottom & Stannard.

Been a - round_____ the world,_____

been a - round_____ the world._____

1. Seen the seas, se - ven, sailed a - cross them all._____
(Verse 2 see block lyric)

Seen the moon rise ov-er Pa-ris, and I watched it gent-ly fall.

Spoken:
On to the beat, keep moving, never stopping, though sometimes I feel like dropping. Gotta keep on and be strong, avoid the wrong.

'cause in this life you walk alone through the danger zone until you get home.

Verse 2:
Been above the clouds,
That paint the sky.
Stood below the cosmos
And pondered on a why.

Back to the track in fact I'm breaking
Though I never knew that you would turn and walk away to stay
And leave me standing on my own
Far from home, like a nomad, sad bad,
Dreams about togetherness that we never had.

LET IT RAIN

Words & Music by Mortimer, Kean, Harding & Curnow.

love, let it rain, love, let it rain, let it rain.

To Coda ⊕

N.C.

1. Damn, get set for da - mage, pre -
(Verse 2 see block lyric)

pare the soul_ to con-trol and ma - nage, cut the groove,—make it rough like a chain - saw, in -

ject a beat,— eat meat— like a car - ni- vore. Trum - pets sound and the wrath pours down,

an - gels dance— to the new groove in town. Clouds part,— sky op - ens wide, no

Am

place to run— and no place to hide.— Love rains down on— me,— don't want to

Verse 2:

Tribes 1 4 4 on the mount

Like an exodus to the final count

Music is blasting, silence everlasting

The call of the cosmos got the planets dancing

To send a new vibe, new ray, new day

A spiritual experience is gonna come your way

A vision, a vibe with a touch too tender

Your love to the lord, now it's time to surrender.

BE THERE

Words & Music by Mortimer, Kean & Hawken.

43

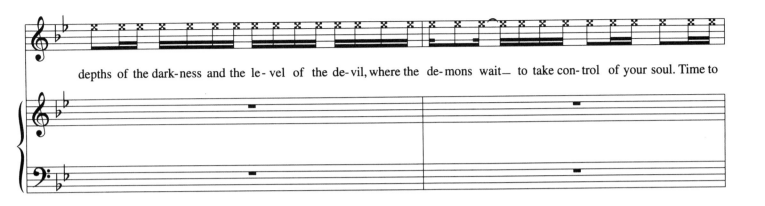

depths of the dark-ness and the le-vel of the de-vil, where the de-mons wait— to take con-trol of your soul. Time to

wise up, rise up and op-en your in-ner eyes up, find hea-ven is a state of mind,— the

D.%. repeat chorus to fade

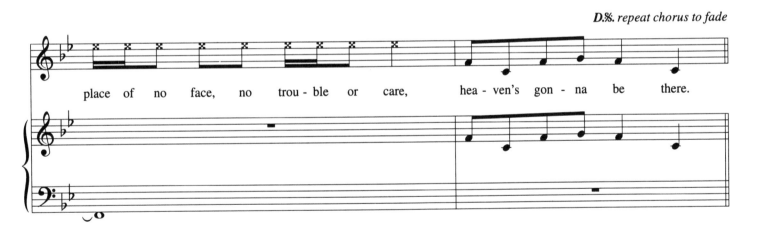

place of no face, no trou-ble or care, hea-ven's gon-na be there.

Verse 2:
Hold a dream against the wind
Close your eyes and let it in
Oh don't try to cross the sea
Don't try to follow me
'Cause I know
It will be there.

M.F. POWER

Words & Music by Mortimer.

Stop, step back as I da-mage your brain,— heart
(Verses 2 & 3 see block lyric)

have an at-tack— but can ya take the pain— I'm go-ing so low, where ya gon-na go, what are ya gon-na do,

To Coda ⊕

C sus⁴

47

Love ain't no-thin' but pow - er.

Love ain't no-thin' but pow - er.

Csus4

Love ain't no-thin' but pow - er.

1.

2.

D.%. al Coda

48

⊕ Coda

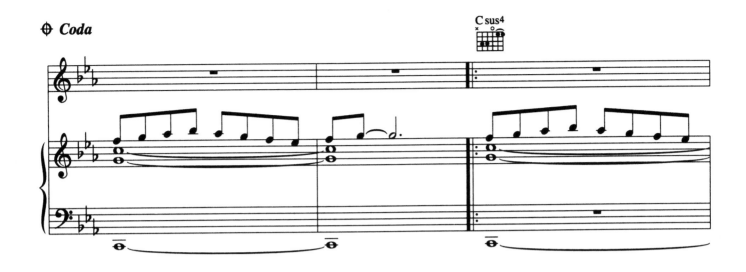

Repeat to fade

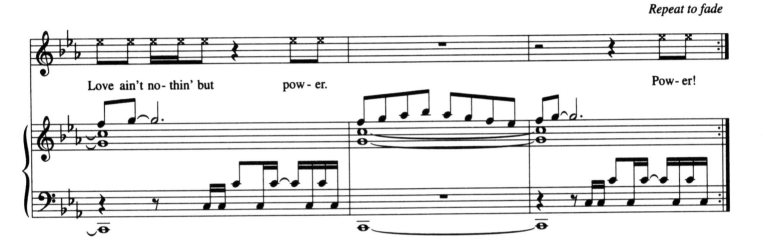

Love ain't no-thin' but   pow-er.   Pow-er!

Verse 2 :
Kids on the corner got a new role model
Rizzla called skins, swigging lager from da bottle
Hanging out in stolen cars, behind bars
They're out on the street, they're selling drugs to get by
Peddling, pushing, call it what you will, they get high
Some wanna kill another life
Before it's begun; you gotta warn 'em quick
Before it's done.

Verse 3:
Born with a spoon in your mouth
From your mother torn they should have never pulled you out
I'm not flowing with the flavour that I gave you for fun
I'm just exploding on the microphone, unloading like a gun
I'm like a demon devil rebel with the level and the treble
Never slowing or stopping or dropping lines like a beginner
I'm a 12″ boar today
And I can blow you away. . .

GENERATION XTC

Words & Music by Mortimer, Kean, Harding & Curnow.

ge - ne - ra - tion X. T. C.

C' - mon____ and op - en your mind,____ look in - side,____ you're

sure to find____ gar - den of tran - qui - li - ty,____ it's

53

D.%. al Coda

⊕ Coda

Verse 2:
C'mon and shine a light
Oh children of a promised land.
Your birth was your right
To the realm of dreams that lay at hand.

9/95 (22528)